CHICKEN-FRIED FUDGE

and other cartoon delights

SBS SCHOLASTIC BOOK SERVICES
NEW YORK TORONTO LONDON AUCKLAND SYDNEY

To my wife Shava

1st printing ....November 1971
Printed in the U.S.A.

"I DON'T BELIEVE I'VE EVER SEEN A CASE OF HAIL DAMAGE QUITE LIKE THIS!"

"IT'S A HAND-KNITTED WALLET!"

" I FIXED <u>THAT</u> MOSQUITO !"

"I KNEW IT WOULD COME TO THIS!"

"THEIRS IS A STRANGE AND WONDERFUL RELATIONSHIP— SHE'S STRANGE AND HE'S WONDERFUL!"

"I DON'T THINK THIS NEW ICE-CREAM STORE IS GOING TO DO VERY WELL ...."

"WELL? YOU SAID WE WERE GOING DUTCH!"

"MY DAUGHTER TELLS ME
YOU PLAY FOOTBALL."

"I'M RETURNING THIS DRESS—
MY MOTHER APPROVED OF IT."

"DUE TO THE HIGH AIR POLLUTION, FLOODS, MUDSLIDES AND RAGING BRUSHFIRES, OUR ECOLOGY FIELD TRIP HAS BEEN CANCELLED!"

"MAY I HAVE THE
FLYING CARPET TONIGHT, DAD?"

"IF YOU DON'T LIKE MY COOKIES,
DURWOOD, JUST SAY SO!"

"THAT MAY BE A TRIFLE <u>HEAVIER</u> THAN YOU'RE USED TO....LET ME PUT THE <u>OTHER</u> ONE ON!"

"I HEARD YOU WERE A <u>CHEAP DATE</u>, LEONARD,
BUT I DIDN'T BELIEVE IT UNTIL NOW!"

"I'M NO GOOD AT FACES, BUT I
NEVER FORGET A PAIR OF KNEES!"

"HE LOVES ME MADLY—
I LIKE THAT QUALITY IN A BOY!"

"DADDY, GARFINKEL WOULD LIKE HIS
GUITAR __STRINGS__ BACK, ALSO!"

"WELL, SO MUCH FOR LONG SKIRTS."

"MAYBE I DIDN'T BOIL THE SPAGHETTI NOODLES LONG ENOUGH!"

"YOU DON'T KISS AND TELL, DO YOU?"

"I'D BETTER GO, RUTHIE— I'M WAXING
THE KITCHEN FLOOR FOR MOTHER!"

"IT'S NOT A MOUSE—
IT'S JUST A <u>GERBIL</u>!"

"DID YOU <u>ASK</u> THE DOG IF HE WANTED
A HAND-KNITTED SWEATER?"

"THE APPLE TREE DID ITS THING."

"WHEN YOU SAID YOU HAD AN <u>ELECTRIC</u> CAR, I ASSUMED..."

"MAY I HAVE THE
CHARIOT TONIGHT, DAD?"

"MAYBE YOU SHOULD PRACTICE YOUR KARATE OUTSIDE, NORMAN!"

"THIS GUY WRITES THE MOST FANTASTIC LOVE LETTERS I'VE EVER READ!"

"YEAH, I KNOW THE VALUE OF A DOLLAR — 22 CENTS!"

"NOW TRY TO IMAGINE ME AS A BLONDE!"

"DOES THIS MEAN YOU WON'T BE HELPING
ME WITH MY HOMEWORK TONIGHT, LINDA?"

"SCIENTISTS ARE LEARNING TO TALK TO PORPOISES — I WISH I COULD TALK TO MY PARENTS!"

"I COULD GO FOR ROGER
IF HE WEREN'T SO SHY!"

"ONCE AND FOR ALL, CAROLYN—
NO ALLOWANCE INCREASE!"

"NOW LET'S GO OVER IT AGAIN AND
FIND OUT WHERE YOU WENT WRONG!"

"ELVIS WHO?"

"IT'S A <u>SHIRT</u>! I MADE IT FOR YOU
ON MY NEW SEWING MACHINE!"

"IT'S A REAL MONEY TREE, ALL RIGHT—
GENUINE THREE-DOLLAR BILLS!"

"MAY I HAVE THE
DOGSLED TONIGHT, DAD?"

"IF YOU REALLY LOVED ME
YOU'D PUNCH HIM IN THE NOSE!"

"SAY, THIS AIR POLLUTION IS GETTING SERIOUS!"

"THERE NOW! IT DIDN'T TAKE ME
SO LONG TO GET READY, DID IT?"

"I DON'T SUPPOSE YOU KNOW WHO PASTED
THE HAIR-SPRAY LABEL ON THE
BLACK SPRAY PAINT?"

"WALTER LIVES IN A WORLD OF HIS OWN!"

"**SURPRISE!** HAH-HAH-HAH! THE OL' FLASH-GUN GETS 'EM EVERY TIME!"

"I THINK GLORIA SORT OF LIKES YOU."

"WHAT'S THE MATTER—NEVER SEEN
A PERSON DRESSED <u>FASHIONABLY</u>?"

"HE'S NOT EXACTLY PATRICK McGOOHAN, BUT HE DOES HAVE A CAR."

"HAROLD AND I MET AT THE
DRUGSTORE HAIR-SPRAY COUNTER!"

"OUR BASKETBALL DEFLATED. COULD WE BORROW ONE OF YOUR CAKES FOR DRIBBLE PRACTICE?"

"MARJORIE! WHEN YOU TIE-DYE YOUR JEANS, TAKE THEM <u>OFF</u> FIRST!"

"I GUESS INSTEAD OF FILLING THE BAG WITH A LOT OF <u>LITTLE</u> POTATO CHIPS..."

"IMAGINE PEOPLE BELIEVING THAT SPELLS IN THAT OLD BOOK COULD REALLY CONJURE UP <u>DEMONS</u>!"

"IT'S HER PERFUME—SMELLS
JUST LIKE A NEW CAR!"

"WELL, YOU SHOULD HAVE <u>TOLD</u> ME
YOU DON'T LIKE CABBAGE-BURGERS!"

"UH, PARDON ME, MISS..."

"I DON'T WATCH MUCH TELEVISION, EITHER—
HARDLY EVER FROM 6 TO 9 A.M., FOR EXAMPLE!"

"IS THIS THE OFFICE OF THE UNDERGROUND NEWSPAPER?"

"OF COURSE YOU NEVER HEARD OF BACON PUDDING — WE JUST INVENTED IT!"

"DID I HIT A NERVE?"

"GUESS THERE'S NO DOUBT, YOUNG MAN—
YOU WIN THE PRIZE FOR 'MOST UNUSUAL
PET'!"

"SOMEHOW THE OLD <u>ROMANCE</u> HAS GONE OUT OF ARTIFICIAL SATELLITES!"

"HE'S SO CHEAP, HIS IDEA OF A BIG DATE IS WATCHING THEM UNLOAD VEGETABLE TRUCKS AT THE A & P!"

"THERE WASN'T MUCH UNDERGROUND
NEWS THIS WEEK!"

"ANYTIME YOU'RE READY."

"NO WONDER YOU'RE HAVING HEADACHES—
YOUR HEADBAND IS TOO TIGHT!"

"MAY I HAVE THE
HORSE TONIGHT, DAD?"

"MAYBE JUST A SHADE TOO MUCH EYE MAKEUP!"

"OH, LET ME GUESS WHO! PAUL NEWMAN?
GLEN CAMPBELL? PAUL McCARTNEY?"

"GESUNDHEIT!"

"IT'S HOT LEMONADE!"

"WELL, YOU SAID YOU LIKE <u>TALL</u> BOYS!"

"OH, BOB—HOW DO YOU LIKE THE FOUNTAIN PEN I GAVE YOU?"

"MY BOYFRIEND — THE FIRST
OF THE SMALL-TIME SPENDERS!"

"I THINK YOU'VE BEEN READING TOO MUCH SCIENCE-FICTION, ARTHUR!"

"YES, I <u>DID</u> SAY I LIKE
LOW-SLUNG SPORTS CARS, BUT..."

"GEE, WHAT LOVELY WEATHER FOR
HAVING A BIG BANANA SPLIT!"

"IT'S THE NEW 'CONVICT' LOOK!"

"IT FALLS <u>OVER</u> ONCE IN A WHILE,
BUT IT SURE SAVES ON TIRES!"

"IT'S CHICKEN-FRIED FUDGE!"

"REVA ALWAYS HAS TO
OUTDO EVERYONE ELSE!"

"WE'LL BEGIN WITH THE BASICS —
THIS IS AN EGG!"

"ARE YOU ANGRY AT ME, WANDA?"

"MAY I HAVE THE
FLYING SAUCER TONIGHT, DAD?"